A Note to Parents

DK READERS is a compelling program for beginning readers, designed in conjunction with leading literacy experts, including Maureen Fernandes, B.Ed (Hons). Maureen has spent many years teaching literacy, both in the classroom and as a consultant in schools.

Beautiful illustrations and superb full-colour photographs combine with engaging, easy-to-read stories to offer a fresh approach to each subject in the series. Each DK READER is guaranteed to capture a child's interest while developing his or her reading skills, general knowledge and love of reading.

The five levels of DK READERS are aimed at different reading abilities, enabling you to choose the books that are exactly right for your child:

Pre-level 1: Learning to read
Level 1: Beginning to read
Level 2: Beginning to read alone
Level 3: Reading alone
Level 4: Proficient readers

The 'normal' age at which a child begins to read can be anywhere from three to eight years old. Adult participation through the lower levels is very helpful for providing encouragement, discussing storylines and sounding out unfamiliar words.

No matter which level you select, you can be sure that you are helping your child learn to read, then read to learn!

LONDON, NEW YORK, MUNICH,
MELBOURNE AND DELHI

For Dorling Kindersley
Project Editor Heather Scott
Designer Hanna Ländin
Managing Editor Catherine Saunders
Art Director Lisa Lanzarini
Publishing Manager Simon Beecroft
Category Publisher Alex Allan
Production Editor Clare McLean
Production Controller Poppy Newdick

For Lucasfilm
Executive Editor Jonathan W. Rinzler
Art Director Troy Alders
Keeper of the Indycron Leland Chee
Director of Publishing Carol Roeder

Reading Consultant
Maureen Fernandes

First published in Great Britain in 2009 by
Dorling Kindersley Limited, 80 Strand,
London, WC2R 0RL

2 4 5 8 10 9 7 5 3 1
DD546 – 07/09

Published in the USA by DK Publishing

A CIP catalogue record for this book
is available from the British Library

ISBN: 978-1-40534-432-6

Color reproduction by MDP, UK
Printed and bound in China by L-Rex

Discover more at
www.dk.com
www.starwars.com

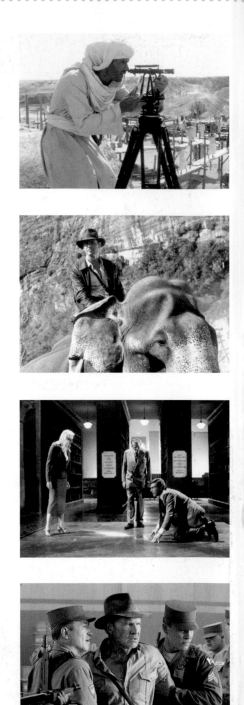

DK READERS

BEGINNING TO READ ALONE

2

Traps and Snares

Written by Clare Hibbert

Join Indiana Jones on his travels in search of treasure. Indy looks for many precious objects around the world.

The searches are never easy. Indy often sets off traps. Oh no! This time a giant ball of rock is rolling after him!

In Peru, Indy is on the trail of
a golden idol. He soon finds out
what happened to his friend,
Doctor Forrestal. He crossed
a beam of sunlight, which set
off spring-loaded spears. Quick
and deadly! Only Forrestal's
skeleton remains.

Sinister statue
This statue is located near the temple entrance to scare people away.

Indy soon finds out that he has more to fear than spears. Many of the stone tiles on the floor are traps, too. If Indy steps on one, poison-tipped arrows shoot at him from the walls.

Indy now understands that the whole temple is booby-trapped. If he removes the idol, he knows something terrible will happen.

Indy wants to trick the temple. He has a little sack of sand. His plan is to switch the idol for the sack, which weighs about the same. At least, he hopes it weighs the same. Oh no! The sand is too heavy!

Golden idol

The stone altar that holds the icon lowers into its base. Indy has set off a chain reaction that causes the ancient temple to seal itself. Indy barely escapes – but then he is chased by a tribe of angry Hovitos.

Oh no! Indy falls off the edge of a cliff while on top of a tank. He jumps off the tank just in time and grabs a tree root.

Indy is looking for the Holy Grail. It is hidden in an ancient temple. When the Grail is carried over a sacred mark on the ground, an earthquake starts! Indy falls into a crack in the rocks. The Grail is almost within Indy's grasp – but he might fall if he tries to reach it!

Indy's hunt for a sacred stone takes him to Pankot Palace. With his friend, Short Round, he explores a secret passage. Where does it lead? Someone does not want them to know. The two are trapped in a mysterious room!

Pankot Palace

Poor Short Round leans against a stone set into the wall. Uh oh! Now the ceiling starts coming down – with spikes!

Hidden temple

The traps keep outsiders from a temple. Here, worshippers sacrifice people to their goddess, Kali.

Indy, Willie and Short Round free the children forced to work in the terrible mines of Pankot Palace.

Now they are stuck in a runaway mine car. Indy jumps out and stops the mine car with his feet.

Evil priest

Indy escapes from the priest, Mola Ram. Indy has taken back the sacred stones.

Then a huge water tank is tipped over. Water gushes through the tunnels. The three find a way out just in time. A moment later, the flood bursts out of the tunnel – and almost knocks them off the cliff.

Imagine being trapped on a rickety old rope bridge, surrounded by enemies. Hungry crocodiles wait below. What would you do?

Indy cuts through the rope – and clings on for dear life.

Rope bridge

The broken bridge swings against the cliff. Indy struggles with Mola Ram. The priest wants the sacred stones in Indy's satchel. Mola Ram loses his grip and falls into the river. The crocodiles gobble him up.

For Indy, even a plane can be a trap. After he escapes the Hovitos tribe, he finds a snake in his seat! Indy is afraid of snakes. He and Marion need to escape from Egypt in a plane. But first Indy must face an angry mechanic.

On another
adventure, Indy,
Willie and Short
Round are on a
plane. But the
pilots empty the
fuel, take the only parachutes
and jump out. Indy is trapped
onboard with a cargo of
squawking chickens!

Life-saving raft
Indy jumps from the
plane with an inflatable
raft. They go whooshing
over snowy slopes
and waterfalls!

Indy is as brave as they come, but he isn't crazy about snakes. As a boy he had no fear. But that all changes the day he falls into a box full of the slithering reptiles! He is completely covered with snakes!

Creepy cobra
Poor Indy. He's always coming face to face with sinister snakes. This cobra is a bit too close for comfort.

In Egypt, Indy sneaks into a place called the Well of Souls. The floor is a sea of snakes. His flaming torch keeps the scary serpents away for a little while. But when the flame goes out, the snakes start to close in.

Indy meets more than his fair share of creepy crawlies and scary animals.

In Venice, Indy and Elsa are looking for a knight's tomb. They step along flooded tunnels that are plagued with rats.

The rainforest has the deadliest bugs. Indy and his guide, Satipo, are covered with tarantulas. And Indy's enemy, Colonel Dovchenko, is attacked by red ants.

Red ant

Jagged jaws

Indy and his father, Henry, are on a beach. Suddenly, they are fired on by a German plane. Surely there is no escape this time! But Henry has an idea. He flaps his umbrella at the seagulls. The frightened flock flies into the air and makes the plane crash.

When Indy was a boy scout, he uncovered a plot to steal the Cross of Coronado. But he grabs the cross and escapes onto a circus train. The thieves chase him, but Indy gets away again.

Indiana Jones teams up with his son, Mutt, on a quest to find Akator, the Lost City Of Gold.

Indy wants to return a strange Crystal Skull to the ancient temple. But many traps and snares block his path. In a round tower, the adventurers must dash down the steps before they disappear into the wall. If Indy isn't fast enough, he will fall onto spikes below.

Hordes of Ugha warriors ambush Indy and his friends in a secret tunnel. They run after Indy, Professor Oxley and Mutt.

Don't trip, Mutt!

It's not the first time Indy's been ambushed. After finding the golden idol, he thinks he's safe once he exits the temple.

Not so! Suddenly he is face-to-face with a tribe of Hovitos. They

are armed with poison arrows.
Run, Indy!

Being double-crossed by a friend
is one of the worst traps of all.
Mac betrays Indy at a secret
army base.

Mac sides with the Russians, so
Indy is forced to find a mysterious
box for Colonel Spalko.

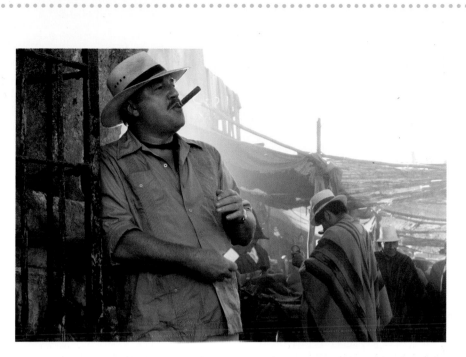

Later, Mac convinces Indy that he is a double agent. It's a trick! Mac is leaving a trail so the Russians can follow Indy.

Power seeker

Spalko will stop at nothing to gain power. But this power destroys her and Mac in the end.

Fascinating Facts

• The monkey that becomes Marion's pet in Cairo is a false friend. It is really a spy, keeping tabs on Indy for a shadowy assassin.

• Indy guesses that there are secret tunnels beneath Pankot Palace. He notices a breeze blowing the flowers in Willie's room.

• To reach the Grail, Indy must make a leap of faith. What looks like a gaping chasm is really spanned by an invisible bridge.

• The glittering grails around the true Grail are traps. When Walter Donovan chooses a fake, it doesn't give him long life – it kills him.

• Indy and Mutt face an array of traps and snares while they search for a grave. There are venomous scorpions, and a 'dead end' that turns out to be a tilting stone.